Supporting Maths

FOR AGES 6–7

Andrew Brodie

Introduction

Supporting Maths is aimed at all those who work with children who have been identified as needing 'additional' or 'different' support in mathematics. It can be used by anyone working with children who fall into this category, whether you are a teacher, classroom assistant or parent.

Typically the six to seven year-old children for whom the book is intended will be working at the levels expected of Foundation Stage or Year 1 children or they may simply need extra help in tackling the level of work appropriate for Year 2. Their difficulties may be short term, and overcome with extra practice and support on a one-to-one or small group basis, or they may be long term, where such support enables them to make progress but at a level behind their peer group. The Record and Review sheet on page 5 is ideal for keeping track of the targets you set and the progress made by each child.

The 2006 Framework for Teaching Mathematics specifies seven strands of learning:

Strand 1   Using and applying mathematics
Strand 2   Counting and understanding number
Strand 3   Knowing and using number facts
Strand 4   Calculating
Strand 5   Understanding shape
Strand 6   Measuring
Strand 7   Handling data

This book addresses all seven strands, drawing on the Key Stage 1 objectives. Particular emphasis is placed on understanding number, using number facts and calculating with these. The *Individual record sheet* on page 3 shows the aspects of the seven strands that can be assessed through using the worksheets and through discussion with the pupil.

In this book we provide activities that can be effectively completed on paper, with the help of an adult. The interaction with the adult gives many opportunities for speaking and listening. Explanation by an adult to a child and vice versa provides a firm foundation for mathematical understanding. To reinforce understanding, many activities should be completed in a practical context e.g. children could count real items; they could compare sizes of real objects; they could perform practical addition by combining two groups of objects; they could perform subtractions by removing objects from a set and seeing how many remain.

Several worksheets deal with counting. Accurate counting is a **vital** skill and is sometimes neglected. Its importance should not be underestimated as many children fail to develop effective strategies for counting. Once these children are asked to perform calculations such as additions and subtractions their inability to count accurately can result in errors. Thus, although they may be able to cope with a particular number operation, these counting errors result in incorrect answers and cause the children to lose confidence in their ability to perform the operation itself. Many activities address the key skills of adding and subtracting. Pupils are supported by the pictures of animals, shapes and other objects on the worksheets and by the 'number ladders', which form useful number lines to help in the visualisation of adding and subtracting.

However you decide to use these sheets and in whatever context, it is worth remembering that children generally achieve the greatest success in an atmosphere of support and encouragement. Praise from a caring adult can be the best reward for the children's efforts. The worksheets and activities in this book will provide many opportunities for children to enjoy their successes. (As a visual reminder, children can also complete the *My record sheet* on page 4). The development of a positive attitude and the resulting increase in self-esteem will help them with all of their school work and other areas of school life too.

Individual record sheet

Name:

Worksheet	Contents	Teaching and learning objective	Target achieved	Needs more practice
1-4	Counting	Strands 1, 2		
5-7	Adding with number ladders	Strands 1, 2, 3, 4		
8-10	Subtracting with number ladders	Strands 1, 2, 3, 4		
11-12	Adding and subtracting	Strands 1, 2, 3, 4		
13	Doubles	Strands 1, 2, 3, 4		
14-18	Number tracks	Strands 1, 2, 3, 4		
19-20	Estimating and counting	Strands 1, 2, 3		
21-26	Number patterns	Strands 1, 2, 4		
27-29	Number order	Strands 1, 2		
30	Put the numbers in order	Strands 1, 2		
31	The 2 times table	Strands 1, 2, 3, 7		
32	The 5 times table	Strands 1, 2, 3, 7		
33	The 10 times table	Strands 1, 2, 3, 7		
34-37	Estimating and counting	Strands 1, 2, 3		
38-39	Numbers on a clock face	Strands 1, 2, 3, 5, 6		
40-41	Write the o'clock times	Strands 2, 5, 6		
42-43	Write the half past times	Strands 2, 5, 6		
44	Days of the week	Strand 6		
45	Triangles	Strands 1, 5		
46	Squares	Strands 1, 5		
47	Circles	Strands 1, 5		
Resource sheet A	Number ladders	Strands 1, 2, 3, 4		
Resource sheet B	Number track race	Strands 1, 2		
Resource sheet C	A hundred square	Strands 1, 2, 4		
Resource sheet D	2 times table	Strands 1, 2, 3, 7		
Resource sheet E	5 times table	Strands 1, 2, 3, 7		
Resource sheet F	10 times table	Strands 1, 2, 3, 7		
Resource sheets G-H	O'clock times	Strand 6		
Resource sheets I-J	Half past times	Strand 6		
Resource sheet K	The clock face	Strands 2, 6		
Resource sheet L	Clock number and days of the week	Strands 2, 6		

My record sheet

Name: _____   Date of birth: _____

Class: _____   Date: _____

I can...

- say and use the number names in order up to 20 ☐
- say and use the numbers names in order up to 30 ☐
- say and use the number names in order up to 100 ☐
- read and write numbers to at least 20 ☐
- read and write the multiples of 10 ☐
- position numbers on a number track and a number line ☐
- estimate numbers of objects and check by counting ☐
- count on in ones ☐
- count on in twos ☐
- count on in fives ☐
- count on in tens ☐
- find one more or one less than another number ☐
- derive and recall all pairs of numbers with a total of ten ☐
- derive and recall addition and subtraction facts for totals to at least 5 ☐

- recall the doubles of all numbers to at least ten ☐
- compare and order numbers ☐
- add a one-digit number to a one-digit or two-digit number ☐
- subtract a one-digit number from a one-digit or two-digit number ☐
- use 'counting on' to find the difference ☐
- use vocabulary and symbols in addition number sentences ☐
- use vocabulary and symbols in subtraction number sentences ☐
- derive the multiples of 2 to the tenth multiple ☐
- derive the multiples of 5 to the tenth multiple ☐
- derive the multiples of 10 to the tenth multiple ☐
- visualise, name and describe the features of 2D shapes ☐
- use vocabulary related to time ☐
- read time to the hour ☐
- read time to the half-hour ☐
- order the days of the week ☐
- record information in lists and tables ☐

Andrew Brodie: Supporting Maths © A & C Black Publishers Ltd. 2007

Record and Review

Name: _____ Date of birth: _____

Teacher: _____ Class: _____

Support assistant: _____

Code of Practice stage: _____ Date targets set: _____

Target

1 _____

2 _____

3 _____

4 _____

Review

Target

1 _____

_____

_____ Target achieved? ☐ Date: _____

2 _____

_____

_____ Target achieved? ☐ Date: _____

3 _____

_____

_____ Target achieved? ☐ Date: _____

4 _____

_____

_____ Target achieved? ☐ Date: _____

Name: _____   **Date:** _____

Write the correct number for each picture.
These are the numbers that you will need:

| 1 | 3 | 4 | 7 | 9 | 12 |

Notes for teachers

Target: Solve problems involving counting (Strand 1). Count on in ones; count reliably at least 20 objects; read and write numbers from 0 to at least 20 (Strand 2).

Help the child count the number of animals in each set. S/he may find it helpful to draw a coloured dot on each picture as it is counted. Observe the way the child writes each number, ensuring that s/he holds the pencil correctly and forms the numbers appropriately.

Name: _____

Date: _____

Write the correct number for each picture.
These are the numbers that you will need:

2	5	6	8	11	14

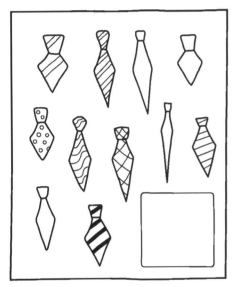

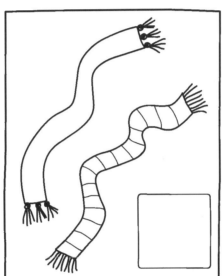

Notes for teachers

Target: Solve problems involving counting (Strand 1). Count on in ones; count reliably at least 20 objects; read and write numbers from 0 to at least 20 (Strand 2).

Help the child count the number of items in each set. S/he may find it helpful to draw a coloured dot on each picture as it is counted. Observe the way the child writes each number, ensuring that s/he holds the pencil correctly and forms the numbers appropriately.

Andrew Brodie: Supporting Maths © A & C Black Publishers Ltd. 2007

Name: _____   **Date:** _____

Write the correct number for each picture
These are the numbers that you will need:

10	13	15	16

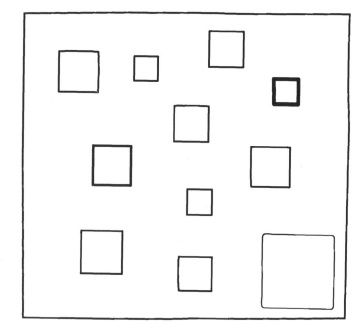

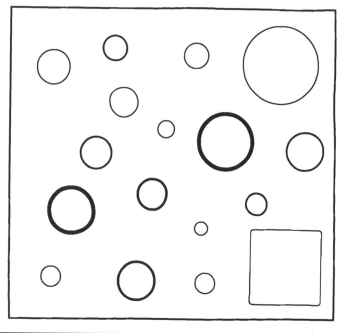

Notes for teachers

Target: Solve problems involving counting (Strand 1). Count on in ones; count reliably at least 20 objects; read and write numbers from 0 to at least 20 (Strand 2). Visualise and name 2-D shapes and describe their features (Strand 5).
Help the child count the number of shapes in each set. S/he may find it helpful to draw a coloured dot on each picture as it is counted. Observe the way the child writes each number, ensuring that s/he holds the pencil correctly and forms the numbers appropriately. Take the opportunity to discuss the names of the shapes in the pictures. Can the child identify triangles, squares and circles?

Write the correct number for each picture.
These are the numbers that you will need:

| 17 | 18 | 19 | 20 |

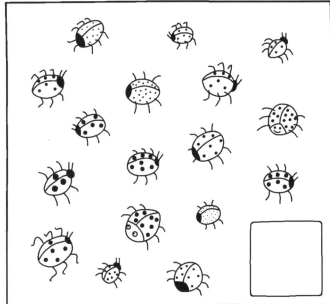

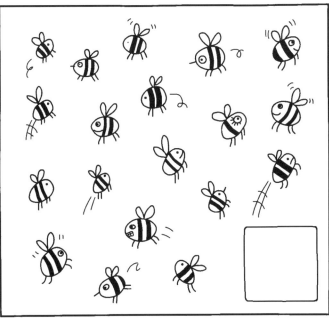

Notes for teachers

Target: Solve problems involving counting (Strand 1). Count on in ones; count reliably at least 20 objects; read and write numbers from 0 to at least 20 (Strand 2).

Help the child count the number of creatures in each set. S/he may find it helpful to draw a coloured dot on each picture as it is counted. Observe the way the child writes each number, ensuring that s/he holds the pencil correctly and forms the numbers appropriately.

4 + 2 = ☐　　　6 + 3 = ☐　　　5 + 2 = ☐

4 + 1 = ☐　　　7 + 2 = ☐　　　3 + 6 = ☐

Notes for teachers

Target: Solve problems involving counting, adding; answer a question by selecting and using suitable equipment (Strand 1). Relate addition to counting on; count on in ones; use the equals sign (Strand 2). Derive and recall all pairs of numbers with a total of 10 and addition facts for totals to at least 5 (Strand 3). Add a one-digit number to a one-digit number (Strand 4).

The ladder makes a useful number line where the child can see that the number goes up when we add and goes down when we subtract. Discuss each question with the child e.g. for the first question, ask the child to start on rung number 4 then to go up 2. S/he should see that this reaches number 6. Some children find it helpful to use a coloured counter. The child should place the counter on the first number used in the addition sentence then move it up the number of 'steps' shown by the second number in the addition sentence. Help the child by saying e.g. 'You are on number four. Now move up two steps'. Encourage the child to notice the number zero which is under the 'one rung'.

6 + 4 = ☐

7 + 3 = ☐

8 + 2 = ☐

9 + 1 = ☐   5 + 5 = ☐   4 + 6 = ☐

Notes for teachers

Target: Solve problems involving counting, adding; answer a question by selecting and using suitable equipment (Strand 1). Relate addition to counting on; count on in ones; use the equals sign (Strand 2). Derive and recall all pairs of numbers with a total of 10 and addition facts for totals to at least 5 (Strand 3). Add a one-digit number to a one-digit number (Strand 4). The ladder makes a useful number line where the child can see that the number goes up when we add and goes down when we subtract. Discuss each question with the child. Some children find it helpful to use a coloured counter. The child should place the counter on the first number used in the addition sentence then move it up the number of 'steps' shown by the second number in the addition sentence. Help the child by saying, 'you are on number six. Now move up four steps.' Of course, the answer to each question on this sheet is 10. Discuss this fact after the child has completed the questions. Point out that four add six gives the same answer as six add four. An extension activity would be for the child to experiment with the other combinations e.g. 'Does three add seven give the same answer as seven add three?' Encourage the child to notice the number zero which is under the 'one rung'.

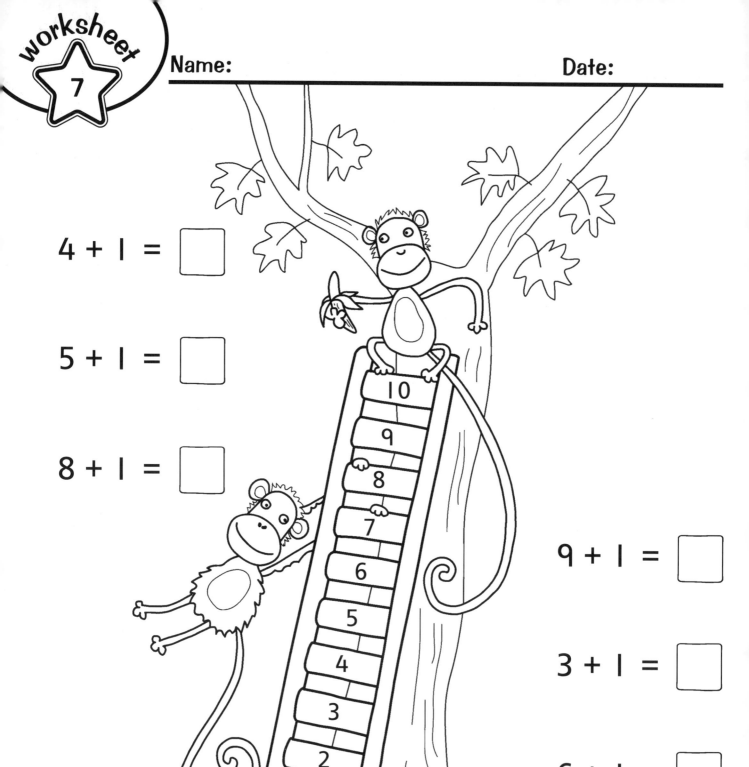

4 + 1 = ☐

5 + 1 = ☐

8 + 1 = ☐

9 + 1 = ☐

3 + 1 = ☐

6 + 1 = ☐

Notes for teachers

Target: Solve problems involving counting, adding; answer a question by selecting and using suitable equipment (Strand 1). Say the number that is one more or one less than any given number; use the equals sign (Strand 2). Derive and recall all pairs of numbers with a total of 10 and addition facts for totals to at least 5 (Strand 3). Add a one-digit number to a one-digit number (Strand 4).

The ladder makes a useful number line where the child can see that the number goes up when we add and goes down when we subtract. Discuss each question with the child. Some children might find it helpful to use a coloured counter. The child should place the counter on the first number used in the addition sentence then move it up one 'step' to find each answer. After completing the answers on the worksheet continue the lesson by asking the child questions such as 'what is one more than seven?' Extend the activity by asking questions such as 'what is one less than five?' Some children will need to use the number ladder to answer these questions. Encourage the child to notice the number zero which is under the 'one rung'.

Name: _____   Date: _____

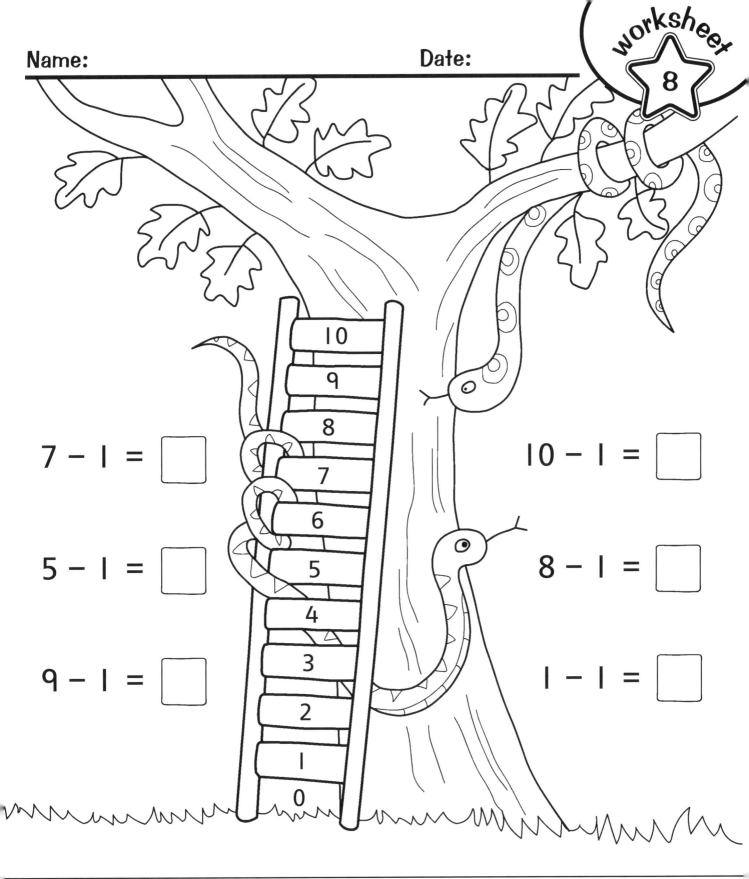

7 – 1 = ☐   10 – 1 = ☐

5 – 1 = ☐   8 – 1 = ☐

9 – 1 = ☐   1 – 1 = ☐

Notes for teachers

Target: Solve problems involving counting, subtracting; answer a question by selecting and using suitable equipment (Strand 1). Say the number that is one more or one less than any given number; use the equals sign (Strand 2). Derive and recall all pairs of numbers with a total of 10 and addition facts for totals to at least 5 and work out the corresponding subtraction facts (Strand 3). Subtract a one-digit number from a one-digit number (Strand 4).

The ladder makes a useful number line where the child can see that the number goes up when we add and goes down when we subtract. Discuss each question with the child. Some children might find it helpful to use a coloured counter. The child should place the counter on the first number used in the subtraction sentence then move it down one 'step' to find each answer. The final question has the answer zero. Some children find the concept of zero very difficult and you may need to discuss the question and the answer with the child. After completing the answers on the worksheet continue the lesson by asking questions such as 'what is one less than three?' Extend the activity by asking questions such as 'what is one more than six?' Some children will need to use the number ladder to answer these questions. Encourage the child to notice the number zero which is under the 'one rung'.

Name: _____ **Date:** _____

7 − 3 = ☐   8 − 4 = ☐   5 − 5 = ☐

9 − 5 = ☐   6 − 1 = ☐   8 − 7 = ☐

Notes for teachers

Target: Solve problems involving counting, subtracting; answer a question by selecting and using suitable equipment (Strand 1). Count back in ones; say the number that is one more or one less than any given number; use the equals sign (Strand 2). Derive and recall all pairs of numbers with a total of 10 and addition facts for totals to at least 5 and work out the corresponding subtraction facts (Strand 3). Subtract a one-digit number from a one-digit number (Strand 4). The ladder makes a useful number line where the child can see that the number goes up when we add and goes down when we subtract. Discuss each question with the child. Some children might find it helpful to use a coloured counter. The child should place the counter on the first number used in the subtraction sentence then move it down the number of 'steps' shown to find each answer. After completing the answers on the worksheet continue the lesson by asking the child questions such as 'what is four take away two?' Some children will need to use the number ladder to answer these questions. Encourage the child to notice the number zero which is under the 'one rung'.

worksheet
10

$10 - 3 =$ ☐ $8 - 5 =$ ☐ $4 - 4 =$ ☐

$3 - 1 =$ ☐ $7 - 3 =$ ☐ $10 - 7 =$ ☐

Notes for teachers

Target: Solve problems involving counting, subtracting; answer a question by selecting and using suitable equipment (Strand 1). Count back in ones; say the number that is one more or one less than any given number; use the equals sign (Strand 2). Derive and recall all pairs of numbers with a total of 10 and addition facts for totals to at least 5 and work out the corresponding subtraction facts (Strand 3). Subtract a one-digit number from a one-digit number or two-digit number (Strand 4). The ladder makes a useful number line where the child can see that the number goes up when we add and goes down when we subtract. Discuss each question with the child. Some children find it helpful to use a coloured counter: the child should place the counter on the first number in the subtraction sentence then move it down the number of 'steps' shown to find each answer. After completing the answers on the worksheet continue the lesson by asking the child questions such as 'what is eight take away three?' Some children will need to use the number ladder to answer these questions. Encourage the child to notice the number zero which is under the 'one rung'.

Name: _____   **Date:** _____

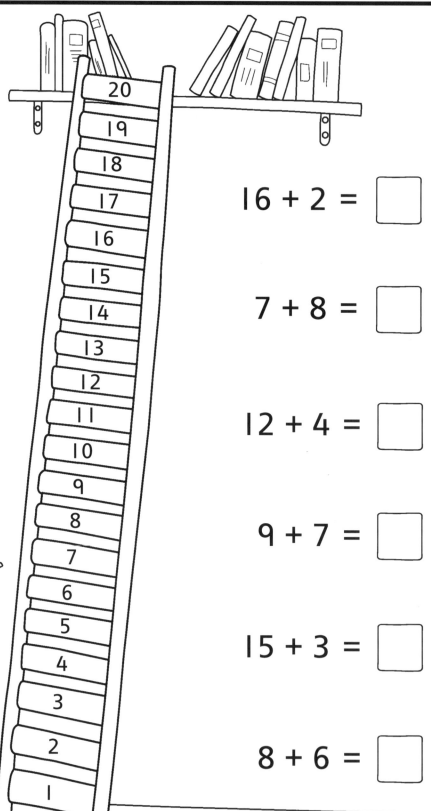

$16 + 2 =$ ☐

$7 + 8 =$ ☐

$12 + 4 =$ ☐

$9 + 7 =$ ☐

$15 + 3 =$ ☐

$8 + 6 =$ ☐

Notes for teachers

Target: Solve problems involving counting, adding; answer a question by selecting and using suitable equipment (Strand 1). Relate addition to counting on; count on in ones; use the equals sign (Strand 2). Add a one-digit number to a one-digit or two-digit number (Strand 4).

The ladder makes a useful number line where the child can see that the number goes up when we add and goes down when we subtract. Discuss each question with the child. Some children might find it helpful to use a coloured counter. The child should place the counter on the first number used in the addition sentence then move it up the number of 'steps' shown by the second number in the addition sentence. Help the child by saying e.g. 'You are on number sixteen, now move up two steps.' Extend the activity by asking questions such as 'thirteen add six' – the child can use the number ladder to find the answers. Encourage the child to notice the number zero which is under the 'one rung'.

14 − 2 = ☐

17 − 9 = ☐

12 − 5 = ☐

13 − 6 = ☐

11 − 7 = ☐

14 − 3 = ☐

Notes for teachers

Target: Solve problems involving counting, subtracting; answer a question by selecting and using suitable equipment (Strand 1). Count back in ones; use the equals sign (Strand 2). Subtract a one-digit number from a two-digit number (Strand 4). The ladder makes a useful number line where the child can see that the number goes up when we add and goes down when we subtract. Discuss each question with the child. Some children might find it helpful to use a coloured counter. The child should place the counter on the first number used in the subtraction sentence then move it down the number of 'steps' shown by the second number in the subtraction sentence. Help the child by saying 'you are on number fourteen, now move down two steps.' Extend the activity by asking questions such as 'fifteen take away seven' – the child can use the number ladder to find the answers. Encourage the child to notice the number zero which is under the 'one rung'.

Name: _____ **Date:** _____

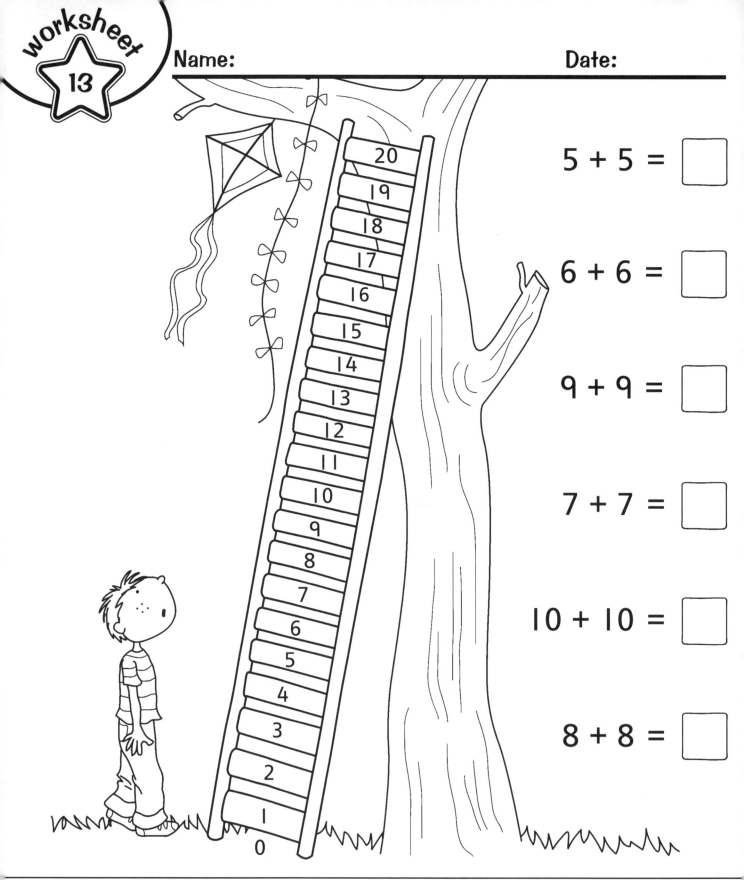

$5 + 5 =$ ☐

$6 + 6 =$ ☐

$9 + 9 =$ ☐

$7 + 7 =$ ☐

$10 + 10 =$ ☐

$8 + 8 =$ ☐

Notes for teachers

Target: Solve problems involving counting, adding; answer a question by selecting and using suitable equipment (Strand 1). Relate addition to counting on; count on in ones; use the equals sign (Strand 2). Recall the doubles of all numbers to at least ten (Strand 3). Add a one-digit number to a one-digit or two-digit number (Strand 4).

The ladder makes a useful number line where the child can see that the number goes up when we add and goes down when we subtract. Discuss each question with the child. Some children might find it helpful to use a coloured counter. The child should place the counter on the first number used in the addition sentence and then move it up the number of 'steps' shown by the second number in the addition sentence. Help the child recognise that the answers show doubles e.g. you could discuss the first question by saying 'six add six is the same as double six'. Extend the activity by asking the child to find the doubles of numbers below five. 'What is double three?' 'What is double one?' etc. Some children will need to use the ladder. To find double three the child may need to put a counter on three then count on three. The speaking and listening that takes place while the child is working is an important aspect of building understanding. Encourage the child to notice the number zero which is under the 'one rung'.

Name: _____   Date: _____

6 + 5 = ☐   5 + 7 = ☐   10 + 4 = ☐

9 + 6 = ☐   8 + 7 = ☐   6 + 6 = ☐

3 + 9 = ☐   7 + 4 = ☐   8 + 5 = ☐

Notes for teachers

Target: Solve problems involving counting, adding; answer a question by selecting and using suitable equipment (Strand 1). Relate addition to counting on; count on in ones; use the equals sign (Strand 2). Recall the doubles of all numbers to at least ten (Strand 3). Add a one-digit number to a one-digit or two-digit number (Strand 4).

This sheet is designed to contrast with the 'number ladder' worksheets and represents the next stage in understanding for some children, leading towards the use of a hundred square. The children can see that here the numbers increase along the track, not in an upward direction as they did on the number ladder. Many children find it helpful to place a counter on the start number then to move on the number of spaces shown by the second number.

Name: _____   **Date:** _____

16 – 4 = ☐   10 – 7 = ☐   10 – 2 = ☐

12 – 8 = ☐   15 – 9 = ☐   13 – 6 = ☐

11 – 5 = ☐   14 – 8 = ☐   12 – 9 = ☐

Notes for teachers

Target: Solve problems involving counting, subtracting; answer a question by selecting and using suitable equipment (Strand 1). Count back in ones; use the equals sign (Strand 2). Derive and recall all addition and subtraction facts for all numbers to at least ten (Strand 3). Subtract a one-digit number from a two-digit number; use strategies such as counting on to find the difference (Strand 4).

This sheet is designed to contrast with the 'number ladder' worksheets and represents the next stage in understanding for some children, leading towards the use of a hundred square. The children can see that here the numbers increase along the track, not in an upward direction as they did on the number ladder. Many children find it helpful to place a counter on the start number then to move back the number of spaces shown by the second number. If the child is confident with this process, show him/her that the questions can be approached in a different way. We can find the difference between the two numbers in the subtraction sentence by starting at the second number, i.e. the smaller one, and counting on to the larger one. Some children will count on incorrectly by including the start number in their counting – this can be avoided by using the counter.

Andrew Brodie: Supporting Maths © A & C Black Publishers Ltd. 2007

$13 - 4 = \boxed{}$ $11 - 3 = \boxed{}$ $14 - 5 = \boxed{}$

$16 - 8 = \boxed{}$ $15 - 7 = \boxed{}$ $12 - 6 = \boxed{}$

$10 - 5 = \boxed{}$ $14 - 6 = \boxed{}$ $16 - 9 = \boxed{}$

Notes for teachers

Target: Solve problems involving counting, subtracting; answer a question by selecting and using suitable equipment (Strand 1). Count back in ones; use the equals sign (Strand 2). Derive and recall all addition and subtraction facts for all numbers to at least ten (Strand 3). Subtract a one-digit number from a two-digit number; use strategies such as counting on to find the difference (Strand 4).

This sheet is designed to contrast with the 'number ladder' worksheets and represents the next stage in understanding for some children, leading towards the use of a hundred square. If you feel that the child is confident with subtraction, show him/her the process of counting on to find the difference by starting at the second number in the subtraction sentence, i.e. the smaller one, and counting on to the larger one. Some children will count on incorrectly by including the start number in their counting – this can be avoided by using the counter.

Write the numbers in the correct places on the number track.

| 1 | 2 | | 4 | 5 | | 7 | | 9 | 10 |

| 11 | 12 | | 14 | | 16 | 17 | | | 20 |

Notes for teachers
Target: Describe simple patterns and relationships involving numbers; answer a question by selecting and using suitable equipment (Strand 1). Compare and order numbers; read and write numbers from 0 to at least 20 – position these on a number track; say the number that is one more or one less than any given number (Strand 2).
This sheet shows a further stage in understanding the relationships between numbers and in using a pictorial representation of these relationships. The children can see that here the numbers increase along the track but that once ten is reached the track starts again. This is the same style of representation as that shown on a hundred square. Take the opportunity to discuss 'one more' or 'one less' e.g. to help the child write the number 3 in the correct place you could ask: 'What number is one more than two? What number is one less than four?'

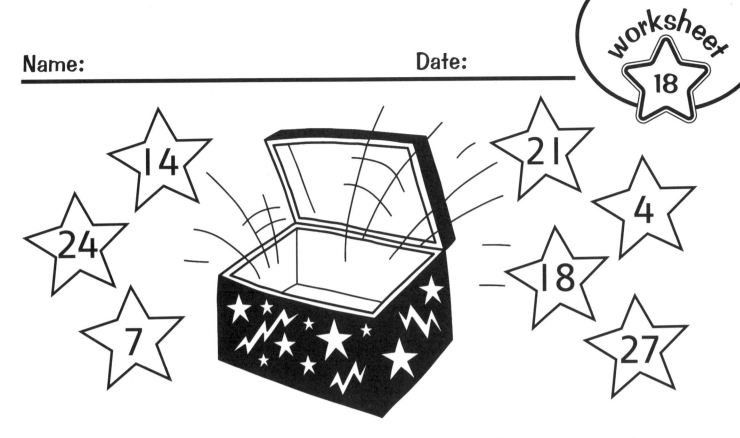

Write the numbers in the correct places on the number track.

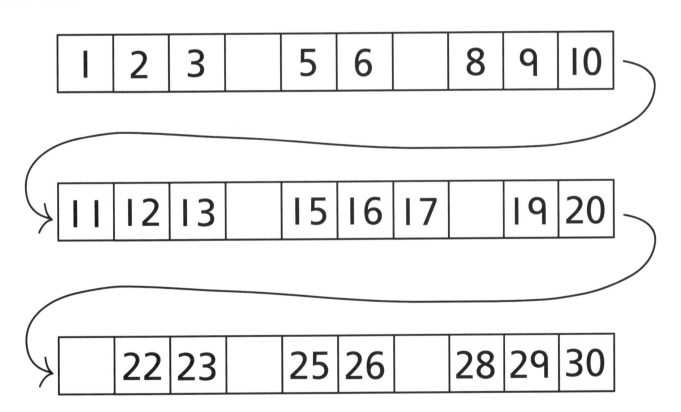

Name: _____   **Date:** _____

How many do you think? ☐

Now count. There are ☐ elephants.

Notes for teachers

Target: Solve problems involving counting (Strand 1). Count reliably at least 20 objects; count on in twos; estimate how many objects and check by counting (Strand 2). Derive the multiples of two (Strand 3).

Ask the child how many elephants s/he thinks there are on the worksheet. Note that many children are not able to make an appropriate estimate but should be praised for making an attempt. Support him/her in writing the appropriate number in the box. Now help the child to count the number of elephants accurately by drawing rings around pairs of elephants then counting in twos. If you feel that the concept of counting in twos is too difficult for a particular child, allow him/her to count using another strategy e.g. s/he could place a counter on each elephant then count the counters. Discuss the actual number of items that the child has counted compared to their first estimate.

Name: _____   **Date:** _____

How many do you think? ☐

Now count. There are ☐ lions.

Notes for teachers

Target: Solve problems involving counting (Strand 1). Count reliably at least 20 objects; count on in twos; estimate how many objects and check by counting (Strand 2). Derive the multiples of two (Strand 3).

Ask the child how many lions s/he thinks there are on the worksheet. Note that many children are not able to make an appropriate estimate but should be praised for making an attempt. Help the child to write the appropriate number in the box. Now help him/her to count the number of lions accurately by drawing rings around pairs of lions then counting in twos. Obviously there is one extra lion, giving a total number of nineteen. If you feel that the concept of counting in twos is too difficult for a particular child, allow him/her to count using another strategy e.g. s/he could place a counter on each lion then count the counters. Discuss the actual number of items that the child has counted compared to their first estimate.

Colour the number 2. Then count on 10 and colour that number. Continue the pattern.

1	2	3	4	5	6	7	8	9	10
11	12	13	14	15	16	17	18	19	20
21	22	23	24	25	26	27	28	29	30
31	32	33	34	35	36	37	38	39	40
41	42	43	44	45	46	47	48	49	50
51	52	53	54	55	56	57	58	59	60
61	62	63	64	65	66	67	68	69	70
71	72	73	74	75	76	77	78	79	80
81	82	83	84	85	86	87	88	89	90
91	92	93	94	95	96	97	98	99	100

Notes for teachers

Target: Describe simple patterns and relationships involving numbers; answer a question by selecting and using suitable equipment (Strand 1). Compare and order numbers; read and write numbers from 0 to at least 20 – position these on a number track; say the number that is one more or one less than any given number; say the number that is ten more or ten less for multiples of ten; count on in ones and tens (Strand 2). Add a multiple of ten to a one-digit or two-digit number; subtract a multiple of ten from a two-digit number (Strand 4).

The hundred square shows another pictorial representation of relationships involving numbers. The children can see that the numbers increase along the row but that once ten is reached they need to look at the start of the next row, etc. Take the opportunity to count up to one hundred with the child, pointing to the numbers on the square as you say them together. The instruction tells the child to colour the number 2. Follow this by asking the child to count on ten and colour that number red, then to count on ten again and colour, etc. Discuss the pattern with the child. S/he should see that the numbers 2, 12, 22, 32, 42, etc are all coloured. Say: 'Two add ten is twelve. Twelve add ten is twenty-two. Twenty-two add ten is thirty-two etc.'

Name: _____   **Date:** _____

Colour the number 4. Then count on 10 and colour that number. Continue the pattern.

1	2	3	4	5	6	7	8	9	10
11	12	13	14	15	16	17	18	19	20
21	22	23	24	25	26	27	28	29	30
31	32	33	34	35	36	37	38	39	40
41	42	43	44	45	46	47	48	49	50
51	52	53	54	55	56	57	58	59	60
61	62	63	64	65	66	67	68	69	70
71	72	73	74	75	76	77	78	79	80
81	82	83	84	85	86	87	88	89	90
91	92	93	94	95	96	97	98	99	100

Notes for teachers

Target: Describe simple patterns and relationships involving numbers; answer a question by selecting and using suitable equipment (Strand 1). Compare and order numbers; read and write numbers from 0 to at least 20 – position these on a number track; say the number that is one more or one less than any given number; say the number that is ten more or ten less for multiples of ten; count on in ones and tens (Strand 2).

Add a multiple of ten to a one-digit or two-digit number; subtract a multiple of ten from a two-digit number (Strand 4). The hundred square shows another pictorial representation of relationships involving numbers. The children can see that the numbers increase along the rows but that once ten is reached they need to look at the start of the next row, etc. Take the opportunity to count up to one hundred with the child, pointing to the numbers on the square as you say them together. The instruction tells the child to colour the number 4. Follow this by asking the child to count on ten and colour that number blue, then to count on ten again and colour, etc. Discuss the pattern with the child. S/he should see that the numbers 4, 14, 24, 34, 44, etc are all coloured. Say: 'Four add ten is fourteen. Fourteen add ten is twenty-four. Twenty-four add ten is thirty-four etc.'

Name: _____   Date: _____

Colour the number 7. Then count on 10 and colour that number. Continue the pattern.

1	2	3	4	5	6	7	8	9	10
11	12	13	14	15	16	17	18	19	20
21	22	23	24	25	26	27	28	29	30
31	32	33	34	35	36	37	38	39	40
41	42	43	44	45	46	47	48	49	50
51	52	53	54	55	56	57	58	59	60
61	62	63	64	65	66	67	68	69	70
71	72	73	74	75	76	77	78	79	80
81	82	83	84	85	86	87	88	89	90
91	92	93	94	95	96	97	98	99	100

Notes for teachers

Target: Describe simple patterns and relationships involving numbers; answer a question by selecting and using suitable equipment (Strand 1). Compare and order numbers; read and write numbers from 0 to at least 20 – position these on a number track; say the number that is one more or one less than any given number; say the number that is ten more or ten less for multiples of ten; count on in ones and tens (Strand 2). Add a multiple of ten to a one-digit or two-digit number; subtract a multiple of ten from a two-digit number (Strand 4).

The hundred square shows another pictorial representation of relationships involving numbers. The children can see that the numbers increase along the rows but that once ten is reached they need to look at the start of the next row, etc. Take the opportunity to count up to one hundred with the child, pointing to the numbers on the square as you say them together. The instruction tells the child to colour the number 7; follow this by asking the child to count on ten and colour that number green, then to count on ten again and colour green, etc. Discuss the pattern with the child. S/he should see that the numbers 7, 17, 27, 37, 47, etc are all coloured. Say: 'Seven add ten is seventeen. Seventeen add ten is twenty-seven. Twenty-seven add ten is thirty-seven etc.'

Colour the number 5. Then count on 5 and colour that number. Continue the pattern.

1	2	3	4	5	6	7	8	9	10
11	12	13	14	15	16	17	18	19	20
21	22	23	24	25	26	27	28	29	30
31	32	33	34	35	36	37	38	39	40
41	42	43	44	45	46	47	48	49	50
51	52	53	54	55	56	57	58	59	60
61	62	63	64	65	66	67	68	69	70
71	72	73	74	75	76	77	78	79	80
81	82	83	84	85	86	87	88	89	90
91	92	93	94	95	96	97	98	99	100

Notes for teachers

Target: Describe simple patterns and relationships involving numbers; answer a question by selecting and using suitable equipment (Strand 1). Compare and order numbers; read and write numbers from 0 to at least 20 – position these on a number track; say the number that is one more or one less than any given number; say the number that is ten more or ten less for multiples of ten; count on in ones and tens (Strand 2). Add a multiple of ten to a one-digit or two-digit number; subtract a multiple of ten from a two-digit number (Strand 4).

The instruction tells the child to colour the number 5. Follow this by asking the child to count on five and colour that number, then to count on five again and colour that number, etc. You may choose to stop the child when s/he reaches 50 or to ask him/her to go on as far as 100. Discuss the pattern with the child. S/he should see that the numbers 5, 10, 15, 20, 25, 30, etc are all coloured. Help the child to count in fives by saying, 'five, ten, fifteen, twenty, etc.'

Colour the number 10. Then count on 10 and colour that number. Continue the pattern.

1	2	3	4	5	6	7	8	9	10
11	12	13	14	15	16	17	18	19	20
21	22	23	24	25	26	27	28	29	30
31	32	33	34	35	36	37	38	39	40
41	42	43	44	45	46	47	48	49	50
51	52	53	54	55	56	57	58	59	60
61	62	63	64	65	66	67	68	69	70
71	72	73	74	75	76	77	78	79	80
81	82	83	84	85	86	87	88	89	90
91	92	93	94	95	96	97	98	99	100

Notes for teachers

Target: Describe simple patterns and relationships involving numbers; answer a question by selecting and using suitable equipment (Strand 1). Compare and order numbers; read and write numbers from 0 to at least 20 – position these on a number track; say the number that is one more or one less than any given number; say the number that is ten more or ten less for multiples of ten; count on in ones and tens (Strand 2).

Add a multiple of ten to a one-digit or two-digit number; subtract a multiple of ten from a two-digit number (Strand 4). The instruction tells the child to colour the number 10. Follow this by asking the child to count on ten and colour that number, then to count on ten again and colour that number, etc. Discuss the pattern with the child. S/he should see that the numbers 10, 20, 30, 40, etc are all coloured. Help the child to count in tens by saying, 'ten, twenty, thirty etc.'

Name: **Date:**

Make your own hundred square.

1									
									100

Notes for teachers

Target: Describe simple patterns and relationships involving numbers; answer a question by selecting and using suitable equipment (Strand 1). Compare and order numbers; read and write numbers from 0 to at least 20 – position these on a number track; say the number that is one more or one less than any given number; say the number that is ten more or ten less for multiples of ten; count on in ones and tens (Strand 2).
For many children this is a very difficult task. If you think that an individual child is capable of completing the hundred square, the task could be of enormous value in strengthening his/her understanding of the relationships between numbers and of the value of each digit in two-digit numbers.

Name: _____   **Date:** _____

Join the dots. Start at number 13.

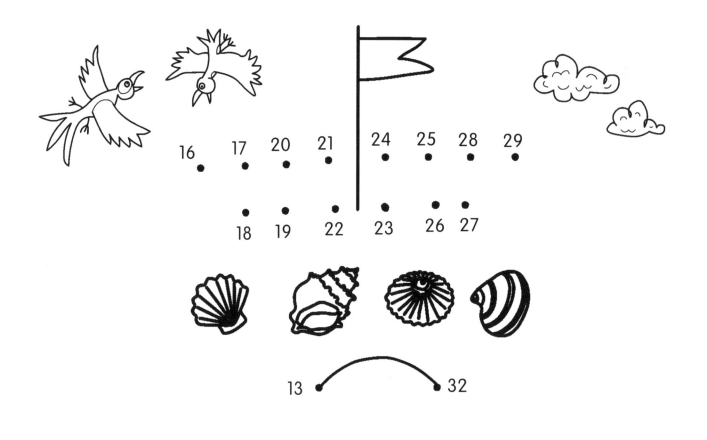

16   17   20   21   24   25   28   29

18   19   22   23   26   27

13   32

15   14   31   30

Notes for teachers

Target: Describe simple patterns and relationships involving numbers (Strand 1). Compare and order numbers; read and write numbers from 0 to at least 20; say the number that is one more or one less than any given number; count on in ones (Strand 2).

This activity helps children to understand the order in which numbers appear. You may like to show the child a hundred square, reminding him/her of the order of the numbers by counting from 13 to 32; encourage him/her to notice that the hundred square starts at 1 but that today s/he is starting at 13.

Join the dots. Start at number 30.

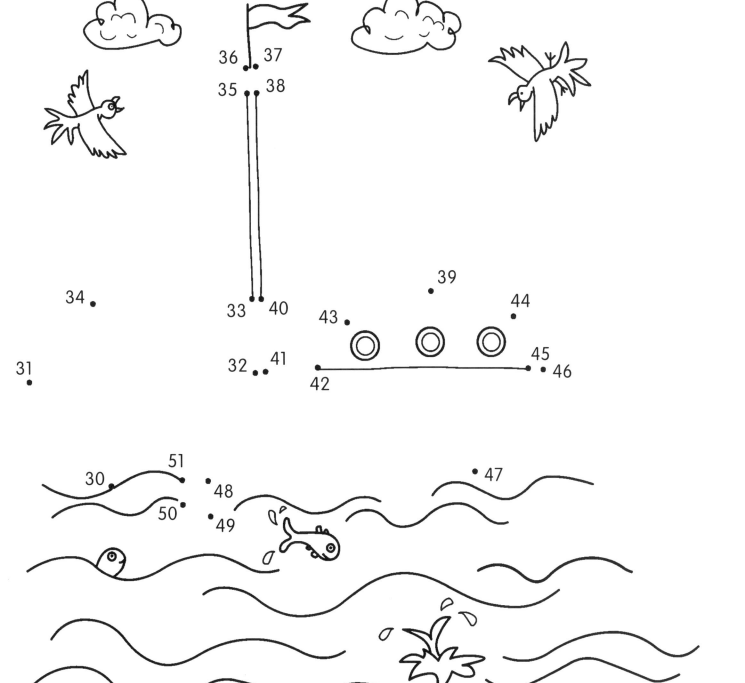

Notes for teachers
Target: Describe simple patterns and relationships involving numbers (Strand 1). Compare and order numbers; say the number that is one more or one less than any given number; count on in ones (Strand 2).
This activity helps children to understand the order in which numbers appear. You may like to show the child a hundred square, reminding him/her of the order of the numbers by counting from 30 to 51. Encourage him/her to notice that the hundred square starts at 1 but that today s/he is starting at 30.

Worksheet 29

Name: _____   **Date:** _____

Join the dots. Start at number 57.

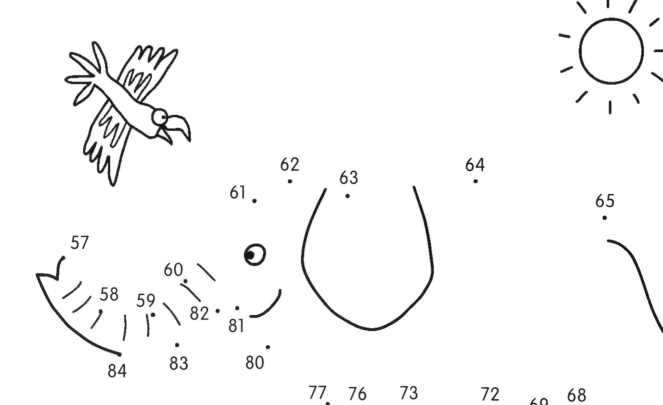

62
61
63
64
65
57
60
58   59
82
81
84   83   80
77   76   73   72   69   68
79   78   75   74   71   70   67   66

Notes for teachers

Target: Describe simple patterns and relationships involving numbers (Strand 1). Compare and order numbers; read and write numbers from 0 to at least 20; say the number that is one more or one less than any given number; count on in ones (Strand 2).

This activity helps children to understand the order in which numbers appear. You may like to show the child a hundred square, reminding him/her of the order of the numbers by counting from 57 to 84. Encourage him/her to notice that the hundred square starts at 1 but that today s/he is starting at 57.

34   Andrew Brodie: Supporting Maths © A & C Black Publishers Ltd. 2007

Put the numbers in order.

14

3

17

10

13

18

7

Notes for teachers
Target: Describe simple patterns and relationships involving numbers (Strand 1). Compare and order numbers; read and write numbers from 0 to at least 20; say the number that is one more or one less than any given number; count on in ones (Strand 2). This activity helps children to understand the order in which numbers appear. Ask the child to cut out the numbers then to place them in order from the smallest to the biggest. The activity provides many opportunities for discussion: 'Which is the smallest of these numbers?' 'Which is the biggest of these numbers?' 'Which of these numbers comes after three?' Etc. You may like to show the child a hundred square to help him/her to decide the order in which to place the numbers.

Name: **Date:**

Complete the 2 times table.

$1 \times 2 = 2$

$2 \times 2 = 4$

$3 \times 2 = \square$

$4 \times 2 = 8$

$5 \times 2 = 10$

$6 \times 2 = \square$

$7 \times 2 = 14$

$8 \times 2 = \square$

$9 \times 2 = 18$

$10 \times 2 = \square$

Notes for teachers

Target: Describe simple patterns and relationships involving numbers; display results using tables (Strand 1). Use the equals sign (Strand 2). Derive the multiples of 2, 5 and 10 to the tenth multiple (Strand 3). Record information in lists and tables (Strand 7).

This sheet can be used to show children how we lay out information in a simple table as well as to help them to practise counting in twos. At this stage we would not expect the children to learn the table off by heart. Please note that mathematically the table should be written in a different format i.e. 2 x 1 = 2, 2 x 2 = 4, 2 x 3 = 6, etc. However the table is traditionally shown in the format that we provide. Help the child in entering the missing numbers. S/he may need to count the dots on the dice but could be encouraged to count in twos.

     Andrew Brodie: Supporting Maths © A & C Black Publishers Ltd. 2007

Name: _____   **Date:** _____

Complete the 5 times table.

$1 \times 5 = 5$

$2 \times 5 = 10$

$3 \times 5 = \boxed{}$

$4 \times 5 = 20$

$5 \times 5 = 25$

$6 \times 5 = \boxed{}$

$7 \times 5 = 35$

$8 \times 5 = \boxed{}$

$9 \times 5 = 45$

$10 \times 5 = \boxed{}$

Notes for teachers

Target: Describe simple patterns and relationships involving numbers; display results using tables (Strand 1). Use the equals sign (Strand 2).Derive the multiples of 2, 5 and 10 to the tenth multiple (Strand 3). Record information in lists and tables (Strand 7).

This sheet can be used to show children how we lay out information in a simple table as well as to help them to practise counting in fives. At this stage we would not expect the children to learn the table off by heart. Please note that mathematically the table should be written in a different format: i.e. 5 x 1 = 5, 5 x 2 = 10, 5 x 3 = 15, etc. However the table is traditionally shown in the format that we provide. Help the child to write in the missing numbers. S/he may need to count the dots on the dice but could be encouraged to count in fives.

Andrew Brodie: Supporting Maths © A & C Black Publishers Ltd. 2007

Name: **Date:**

Complete the 10 times table.

1 x 10 = 10

2 x 10 = ☐

3 x 10 = 30

4 x 10 = ☐

5 x 10 = ☐

6 x 10 = ☐

7 x 10 = ☐

8 x 10 = 80

9 x 10 = ☐

10 x 10 = ☐

Notes for teachers

Target: Describe simple patterns and relationships involving numbers; display results using tables (Strand 1). Use the equals sign (Strand 2). Derive the multiples of 2, 5 and 10 to the tenth multiple (Strand 3). Record information in lists and tables (Strand 7).

This sheet can be used to show children how we lay out information in a simple table as well as to help them to practise counting in tens. At this stage we would not expect the children to learn the table taff by heart. Help the child to write the missing numbers. S/he may need to count the dots on the dominos but could be encouraged to count in tens. Some children will notice that each domino is a 'double five' and should be praised for noticing this. Take the opportunity to discuss that double five is ten.

        Andrew Brodie: Supporting Maths © A & C Black Publishers Ltd. 2007

How many do you think there are?

Now count. There are ☐ parrots.

Notes for teachers

Target: Solve problems involving counting (Strand 1). Count reliably at least 20 objects; count on in fives; estimate how many objects and check by counting (Strand 2). Derive the multiples of five (Strand 3).

Ask the child how many parrots s/he thinks there are on the worksheet. Note that many children are not able to make an appropriate estimate but should be praised for making an attempt. Help the child to write the appropriate number in the box. Now help him/her to count the number of parrots accurately by drawing rings around groups of five parrots then counting in fives. If you feel that the concept of counting in fives is too difficult for a particular child, allow him/her to count using another strategy e.g. s/he could place a counter on each parrot then count the counters. Discuss the actual number of items that the child has counted compared to their first estimate.

Name: **Date:**

How many do you think there are?

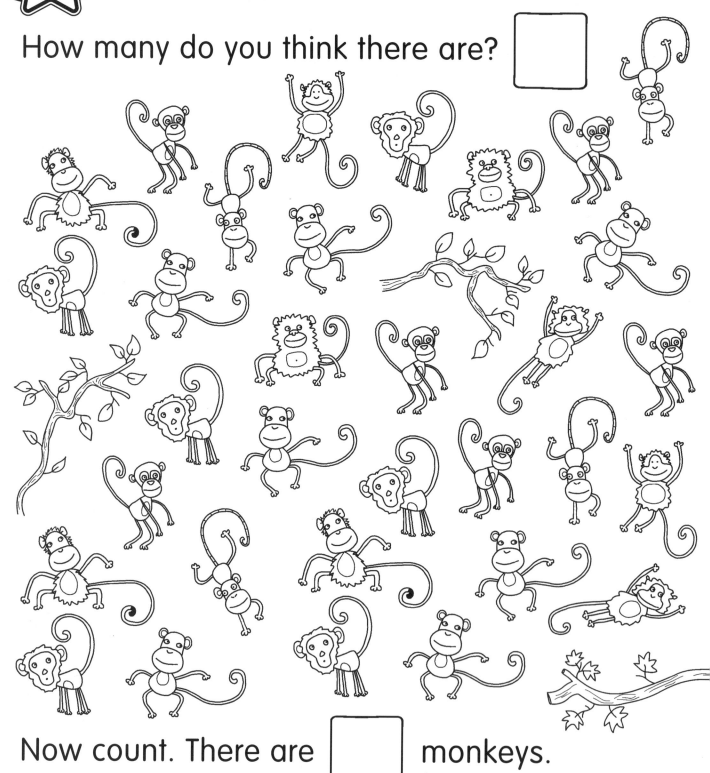

Now count. There are ☐ monkeys.

Notes for teachers

Target: Solve problems involving counting (Strand 1). Count reliably at least 20 objects; count on in fives; estimate how many objects and check by counting (Strand 2). Derive the multiples of five (Strand 3).

Ask the child how many monkeys s/he thinks there are on the worksheet. Note that many children are not able to make an appropriate estimate but should be praised for making an attempt. Help the child to write the appropriate number in the box. Now help him/her to count the number of monkeys accurately by drawing rings around groups of five monkeys then counting in fives. There will, of course, be two monkeys outside the rings making a total of thirty-two. If you feel that the concept of counting in fives is too difficult for a particular child, allow him/her to count using another strategy e.g. s/he could place a counter on each monkey then count the counters. Discuss the actual number of items that the child has counted compared to their first estimate.

Name: _____ **Date:** _____

Look for caterpillars.
How many do you think there are?

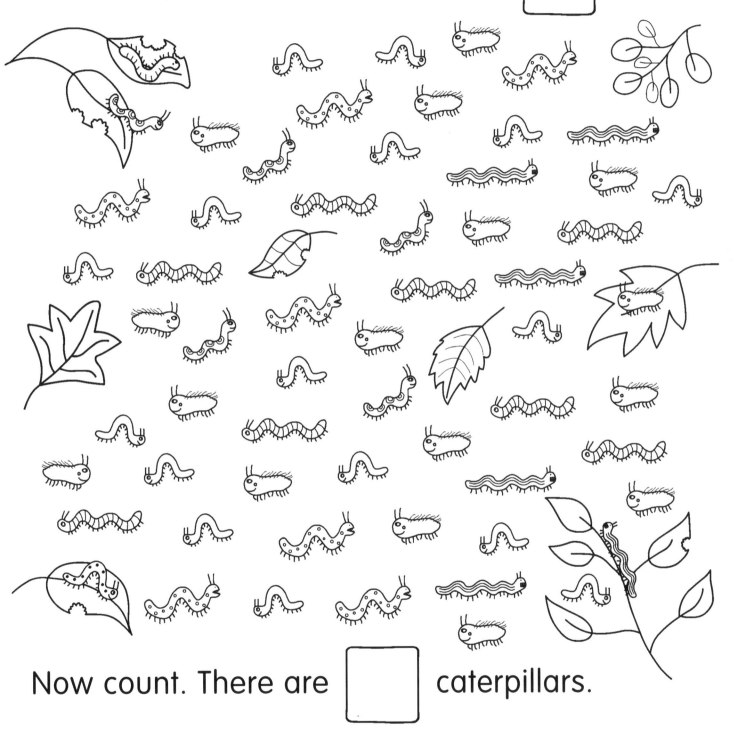

Now count. There are ☐ caterpillars.

Notes for teachers:
Target: Solve problems involving counting (Strand 1). Count up to 100 objects by grouping them in tens; count on in tens; estimate how many objects and check by counting (Strand 2). Derive the multiples of ten (Strand 3).
Ask the child how many caterpillars s/he thinks there are on the worksheet. Note that many children are not able to make an appropriate estimate but should be praised for making an attempt. Help the child to write the appropriate number in the box. Now help him/her to count the number of caterpillars accurately by drawing rings around groups of ten caterpillars then counting in tens. Discuss the actual number of items that the child has counted compared to their first estimate.

Andrew Brodie: Supporting Maths © A & C Black Publishers Ltd. 2007

Name: _____   Date: _____

Look for butterflies.
How many do you think there are?

Now count. There are ☐ butterflies.

Notes for teachers
Target: Solve problems involving counting (Strand 1). Count up to 100 objects by grouping them in tens; estimate how many objects and check by counting (Strand 2). Derive the multiples of ten (Strand 3).
Ask the child how many butterflies s/he thinks there are on the worksheet. Note that many children are not able to make an appropriate estimate but should be praised for making an attempt. Help the child to write the appropriate number in the box. Now help him/her to count the number of butterflies accurately by drawing rings around groups of ten butterflies then counting in tens. There are four extra butterflies giving a total of seventy-four. Discuss the actual number of items that the child has counted compared to their first estimate.

Name: _____ **Date:** _____

Fill in the missing numbers.

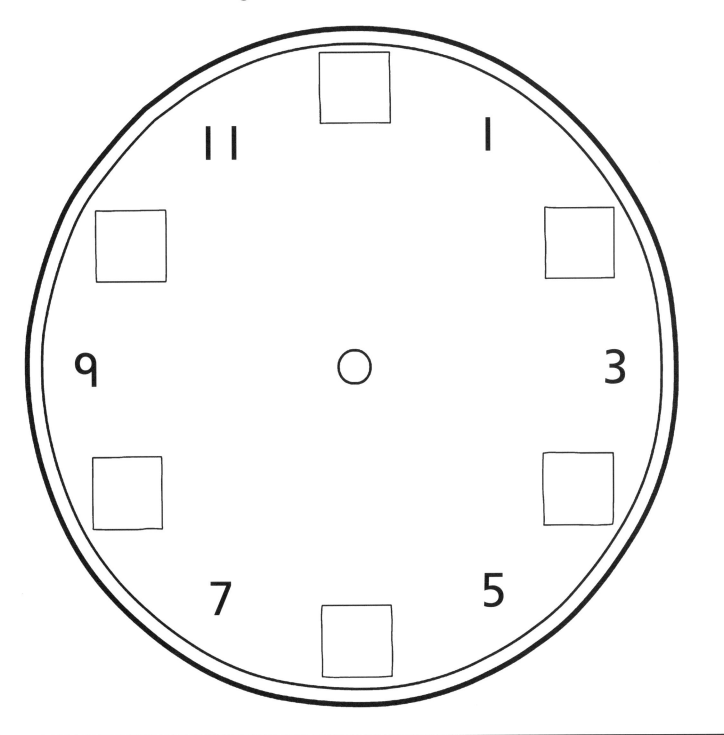

Notes for teachers

Target: Talk about, recognise and recreate simple patterns (Strand 1). Say and use number names; count aloud in ones, twos; read and write numerals and position these numbers on a number track and number line; order numbers, using the related vocabulary; say the number that is one more or less than a given number (Strand 2). Find one more or one less than a number from 1 to 10 (Strand 3). Use everyday words to describe position (Strand 5). Use vocabulary related to time; read time to hour and half-hour (Strand 6).

The clock face is a very useful resource in number work as it provides a familiar number track. Discuss the classroom clock with the child, encouraging him/her to notice the position of the numbers. Read the numbers on the clock on this sheet with the pupil: 1, 3, 5, 7, 9, and 11, thus providing the opportunity to follow a simple number sequence. Discuss which numbers are missing from the clock face. Help the child to write or stick the numbers in the correct places. Numbers of the correct size for this activity can be found on Resource sheet L.

Fill in the missing numbers.

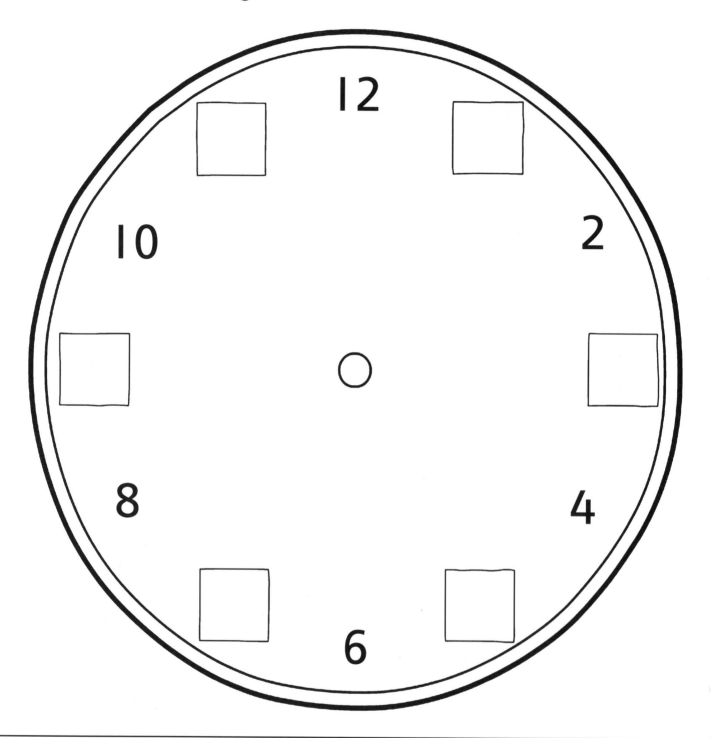

Notes for teachers

Target: Talk about, recognise and recreate simple patterns (Strand 1). Say and use number names; count aloud in ones, twos; read and write numerals and position these numbers on a number track and number line; order numbers, using the related vocabulary; say the number that is one more or less than a given number (Strand 2). Find one more or one less than a number from 1 to 10 (Strand 3). Use everyday words to describe position (Strand 5). Use vocabulary related to time; read time to hour and half-hour (Strand 6).

The clock face is a very useful resource in number work as it provides a number track that children are familiar with. Discuss the classroom clock with the child, encouraging him/her to notice the position of the numbers. Read the numbers on the clock on this sheet with the pupil: 2, 4, 6, 8, 10, and 12, thus providing the opportunity to count aloud in twos. Discuss which numbers are missing from the clock face. Help him/her to write or stick the numbers in the correct places. Numbers of the correct size for this activity can be found on Resource sheet L.

Andrew Brodie: Supporting Maths © A & C Black Publishers Ltd. 2007

Name: _____   **Date:** _____

worksheet 40

Write the o'clock times.

2 o'clock

_____

_____

_____

_____

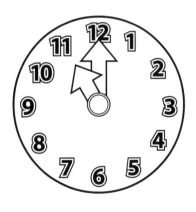

_____

_____

Notes for teachers

Target: Compare and order numbers (Strand 2). Use everyday words to describe position (Strand 5). Use vocabulary related to time; read time to hour and half-hour (Strand 6).

Discuss the hour hand and the minute hand with the child explaining that the minute hand always points to the top of the clock when it is an o'clock time. You may find Resource sheet K helpful for this activity as you can show the appropriate times. The task will be more meaningful to the child if s/he thinks about what happens at particular times of the day.

Andrew Brodie: Supporting Maths © A & C Black Publishers Ltd. 2007

Name: _____ **Date:** _____

Write the o'clock times.

_____ _____

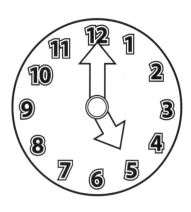

_____ _____

_____ _____

Notes for teachers

Target: Compare and order numbers (Strand 2). Use everyday words to describe position (Strand 5). Use vocabulary related to time; read time to hour and half-hour (Strand 6).

Discuss the hour hand and the minute hand with the child explaining that the minute hand always points to the top of the clock when it is an o'clock time. You may find Resource sheet K helpful for this activity as you can show the appropriate times. The task will be more meaningful to the child if s/he thinks about what happens at particular times of the day.

Name: _____   **Date:** _____

Write the half past times.

half-past 1

_____

_____

_____

_____

_____

Notes for teachers

Target: Compare and order numbers (Strand 2). Use everyday words to describe position (Strand 5). Use vocabulary related to time; read time to hour and half-hour (Strand 6)

Discuss the hour hand and the minute hand with the child explaining that the minute hand always points to the bottom of the clock when it is a half past time. Many children do not understand that the hour hand is halfway between different o'clock times – a real clock where you can move the hands to show the children is an essential resource. They need to realise that the half past time refers to the last o'clock time that the hour hand passed i.e. half past one is half an hour past one o'clock. You may also find Resource sheet K helpful for this activity as you can show the appropriate times. The task will be more meaningful to the child if s/he thinks about what happens at particular times of the day. Note that on this sheet the times shown are in chronological order.

Name: _____ **Date:** _____

Write the half past times.

Notes for teachers

Target: Compare and order numbers (Strand 2). Use everyday words to describe position (Strand 5). Use vocabulary related to time; read time to hour and half-hour (Strand 6).

Discuss the hour hand and the minute hand with the child explaining that the minute hand always points to the bottom of the clock when it is a half-past time. Many children do not understand that the hour hand is halfway between different o'clock times – a real clock where you can move the hands to show the children is an essential resource. They need to realise that the half past time refers to the last o'clock time that the hour hand passed i.e. half past one is half an hour past one o'clock. You may also find Resource sheet K helpful for this activity as you can show the appropriate times. The task will be more meaningful to the child if s/he thinks about what happens at particular times of the day. Note that on this sheet the times shown are in chronological order.

 Andrew Brodie: Supporting Maths © A & C Black Publishers Ltd. 2007

Name: _____ **Date:** _____

Put the days of the week in order.

Wednesday	Friday
Saturday	Monday
Thursday	Sunday
Tuesday	

Notes for teachers

Target: Use vocabulary related to time; order days of the week (Strand 6)
Ask the child to cut out the word tiles then to arrange them in order. You can ask him/her to start on any day e.g. 'Today is Wednesday.' 'Let's find Wednesday.' 'What day comes after Wednesday?' 'What day comes after Thursday?' Etc. You could also discuss what happens on each day of the week and you could extend the activity by asking the child to copy the days out in order.

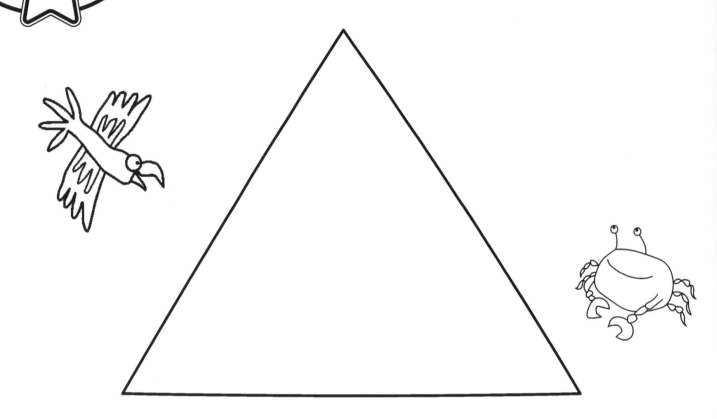

Draw a triangle.

Notes for teachers

Target: Describe simple patterns and relationships involving numbers or shapes (Strand 1). Visualise and name 2D shapes and describe their features; use them to make patterns, pictures and models (Strand 5).

Discuss the picture of the triangle asking questions such as: 'How many sides has the triangle got?' 'How many corners has the triangle got?' 'How long is this side?' (Though we would not expect the child to answer this question in centimetres, we could expect her/him to say 'about the same length as my pencil', for example.) You could ask the child to draw his/her triangle freehand or you may feel that it would be useful for her/him to use a ruler for resting the pencil against – this may be a new activity for the child and a lot of support will be needed.

Name:

Date:

Draw a square.

Notes for teachers

Target: Describe simple patterns and relationships involving numbers or shapes (Strand 1). Visualise and name 2D shapes and describe their features; use them to make patterns, pictures and models (Strand 5)

Discuss the picture of the square asking questions such as: 'How many sides has the square got?' 'How many corners has the square got?' 'How long is this side?' (Though we would not expect the child to answer this question in centimetres, we could expect her/him to say 'about the same length as my pencil', for example.) Discuss the fact that the four sides of the square are all the same length. You could ask the child to draw her/his square freehand or you may feel that it would be useful for her/him to use a ruler for resting the pencil against – this may be a new activity for the child and a lot of support will be needed. If you feel that the child is confident enough you could ask her/him to draw each side 10cm long by measuring against the appropriate mark on the ruler.

Name: _____ **Date:** _____

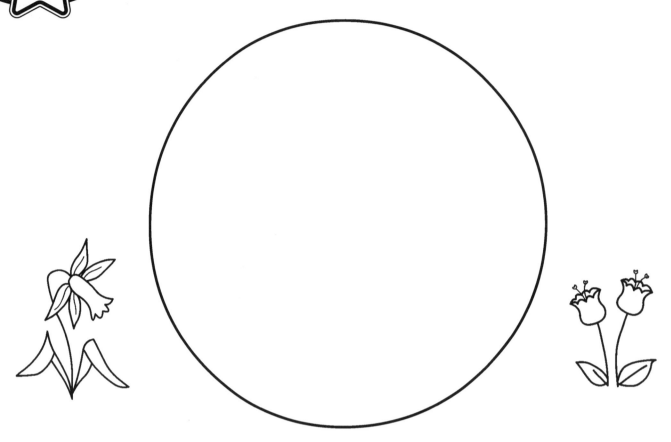

Draw a circle.

Notes for teachers

Target: Describe simple patterns and relationships involving numbers or shapes (Strand 1). Visualise and name 2D shapes and describe their features; use them to make patterns, pictures and models (Strand 5).

Discuss the picture of the circle asking questions such as: 'How many corners has the circle got?' To draw the circle it would be helpful to provide the child with something to draw round but s/he is likely to need support with completing this task.

Resource sheet A

Number ladders

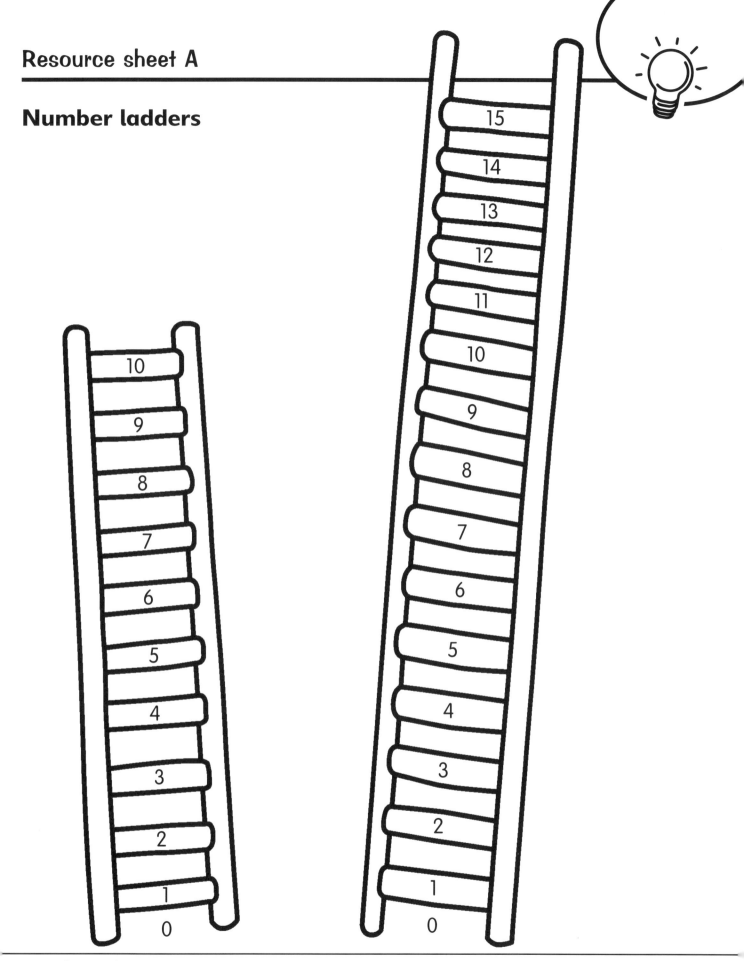

Notes for teachers

Target: Use developing mathematical ideas and methods to solve practical problems; solve problems involving counting, adding; answer a question by selecting and using suitable equipment (Strand 1). Say and use number names; count reliably at least 20 objects; recognise numerals; use the equals sign (Strand 2). Find one more or one less than a number from 1 to 10 (Strand 3). Add mentally a one-digit number to a one-digit or two-digit number; subtract one-digit numbers from one-digit and two-digit numbers (Strand 4).

The ladder makes a useful number line where the child can see that the number goes up when we add and goes down when we subtract. This resource sheet can be used whenever a child has to add or subtract numbers in the range 0 to 15.

Number track race

start

| 1 | 2 | 3 | 4 | 5 | 6 | 7 | 8 | 9 | 10 |

| 11 | 12 | 13 | 14 | 15 | 16 | 17 | 18 | 19 | 20 |

finish

| 21 | 22 | 23 | 24 | 25 | 26 | 27 | 28 | 29 | 30 |

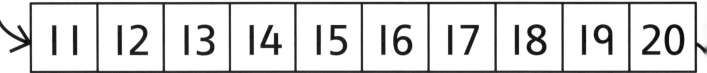

Notes for teachers
Target: Describe simple patterns and relationships involving numbers; answer a question by selecting and using suitable equipment (Strand 1). Compare and order numbers; read and write numbers from 0 to at least 20 – position these on a number track; say the number that is one more or one less than any given number; count on in ones (Strand 2).
This game provides practice in using a number track to 30 in the style of a hundred square. The game is for two players who take it in turns to roll the dice and then move a counter along a track according to the dice throw. The child will benefit from discussion of each move but particularly when 'crossing tens boundaries' i.e. at 10 to 11 and at 20 to 21. The winner is the first to pass 30.

A hundred square

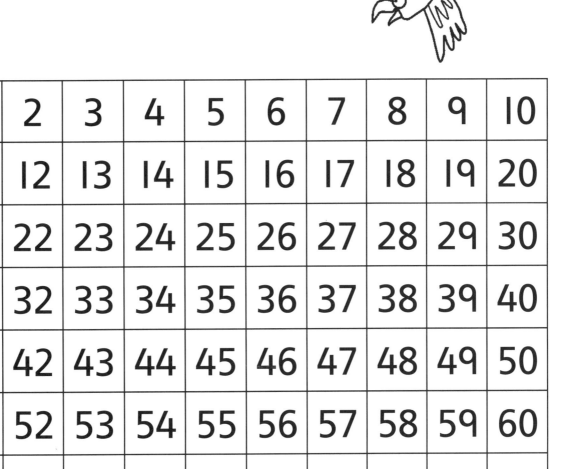

1	2	3	4	5	6	7	8	9	10
11	12	13	14	15	16	17	18	19	20
21	22	23	24	25	26	27	28	29	30
31	32	33	34	35	36	37	38	39	40
41	42	43	44	45	46	47	48	49	50
51	52	53	54	55	56	57	58	59	60
61	62	63	64	65	66	67	68	69	70
71	72	73	74	75	76	77	78	79	80
81	82	83	84	85	86	87	88	89	90
91	92	93	94	95	96	97	98	99	100

Notes for teachers

Target: Describe simple patterns and relationships involving numbers; answer a question by selecting and using suitable equipment (Strand 1). Compare and order numbers; read and write numbers from 0 to at least 20 – position these on a number track; say the number that is one more or one less than any given number; say the number that is ten more or ten less for multiples of ten; count on in ones and tens (Strand 2). Add a multiple of ten to a one-digit or two-digit number; subtract a multiple of ten from a two-digit number (Strand 4).

The hundred square shows a pictorial representation of relationships involving numbers. The children can see that the numbers increase along the row but that once ten is reached they need to look at the start of the next row, etc. This sheet should be photocopied and laminated to create an excellent resource for the child to keep for ready reference.

2 times table

1 x 2 = 2	One times two is two
2 x 2 = 4	Two times two is four
3 x 2 = 6	Three times two is six
4 x 2 = 8	Four times two is eight
5 x 2 = 10	Five times two is ten
6 x 2 = 12	Six times two is twelve
7 x 2 = 14	Seven times two is fourteen
8 x 2 = 16	Eight times two is sixteen
9 x 2 = 18	Nine times two is eighteen
10 x 2 = 20	Ten times two is twenty

Notes for teachers

Target: Display results using tables (Strand 1). Use the equals sign (Strand 2). Derive the multiples of 2, 5 and 10 to the tenth multiple (Strand 3). Record information in lists and tables (Strand 7).

This sheet can be used to show children how we lay out information in a simple table as well as to help them to practise counting in twos. It is suitable for display on the wall so that children can refer to it quickly. At this stage we would not expect the children to learn the table off by heart. Please note that mathematically the table should be written in a different format: i.e., 2 x 1 = 2, 2 x 2 = 4, 2 x 3 = 6, etc. However the table is more usually shown in the format that we provide. Show the children each line of the table as a number sentence and encourage them to read the sentences as 'one times two is two', etc. It can also be helpful to focus on the multiples themselves, supporting the children in saying 'two, four, six, eight', etc.

5 times table

1 x 5 = 5	One times five is five
2 x 5 = 10	Two times five is ten
3 x 5 = 15	Three times five is fifteen
4 x 5 = 20	Four times five is twenty
5 x 5 = 25	Five times five is twenty-five
6 x 5 = 30	Six times five is thirty
7 x 5 = 35	Seven times five is thirty-five
8 x 5 = 40	Eight times five is forty
9 x 5 = 45	Nine times five is forty-five
10 x 5 = 50	Ten times five is fifty

Notes for teachers
Target: Display results using tables (Strand 1). Use the equals sign (Strand 2). Derive the multiples of 2, 5 and 10 to the tenth multiple (Strand 3). Record information in lists and tables (Strand 7).
This sheet can be used to show children how we lay out information in a simple table as well as to help them to practise counting in fives. It is suitable for display on the wall so that children can refer to it quickly. At this stage we would not expect the children to learn the table off by heart. Please note that mathematically the table should be written in a different format: i.e., 5 x 1 = 5, 5 x 2 = 10, 5 x 3 = 15, etc. However, more usually the table is shown in the format that we provide. Show the children each line of the table as a number sentence and encourage them to read the sentences as 'one times five is five', etc. It can also be helpful to focus on the multiples themselves, supporting the children in saying 'five, ten, fifteen, twenty', etc.

10 times table

1 x 10 =	10	One times ten is ten
2 x 10 =	20	Two times ten is twenty
3 x 10 =	30	Three times ten is thirty
4 x 10 =	40	Four times ten is forty
5 x 10 =	50	Five times ten is fifty
6 x 10 =	60	Six times ten is sixty
7 x 10 =	70	Seven times ten is seventy
8 x 10 =	80	Eight times ten is eighty
9 x 10 =	90	Nine times ten is ninety
10 x 10 =	100	Ten times ten is one hundred

Notes for teachers

Target: Display results using tables (Strand 1). Use the equals sign (Strand 2). Derive the multiples of 2, 5 and 10 to the tenth multiple (Strand 3). Record information in lists and tables (Strand 7).

This sheet can be used to show children how we lay out information in a simple table as well as to help them to practise counting in tens. It is suitable for display on the wall so that children can refer to it quickly. At this stage we would not expect the children to learn the table off by heart. Please note that mathematically the table should be written in a different format: i.e., 10 x 1 = 10, 10 x 2 = 20, 10 x 3 = 30, etc. However, more usually the table is shown in the format that we provide. Show the children each line of the table as a number sentence and encourage them to read the sentences as 'one times ten is ten', etc. It can also be helpful to focus on the multiples themselves, supporting the children in saying 'ten, twenty, thirty, forty', etc.

O'clock times

1 o'clock

2 o'clock

3 o'clock

4 o'clock

5 o'clock

6 o'clock

Notes for teachers
Target: Use vocabulary related to time; read time to hour and half-hour (Strand 6).
The time cards have several functions. They can be used for:
- practising numbers in order
- speaking and listening activities describing events in chronological order
- matching to times shown on the clock face that can be created from Resource sheet K

O'clock times

7 o'clock

8 o'clock

9 o'clock

10 o'clock

11 o'clock

12 o'clock

Notes for teachers
Target: Use vocabulary related to time; read time to hour and half-hour (Strand 6).
The time cards have several functions. They can be used for:
• practising numbers in order
• speaking and listening activities describing events in chronological order
• matching to times shown on the clock face that can be created from Resource sheet K

Half past times

half past 1

half past 2

half past 3

half past 4

half past 5

half past 6

Notes for teachers

Target: Use vocabulary related to time; read time to hour and half-hour (Strand 6).

The time cards have several functions. They can be used for:
- practising numbers in order
- speaking and listening activities describing events in chronological order
- matching to times shown on the clock face that can be created from Resource sheet K

Half past times

half past 7

half past 8

half past 9

half past 10

half past 11

half past 12

Notes for teachers
Target: Use vocabulary related to time; read time to hour and half-hour (Strand 6).
The time cards have several functions. They can be used for:
• practising numbers in order
• speaking and listening activities describing events in chronological order
• matching to times shown on the clock face that can be created from Resource sheet K

The clock face

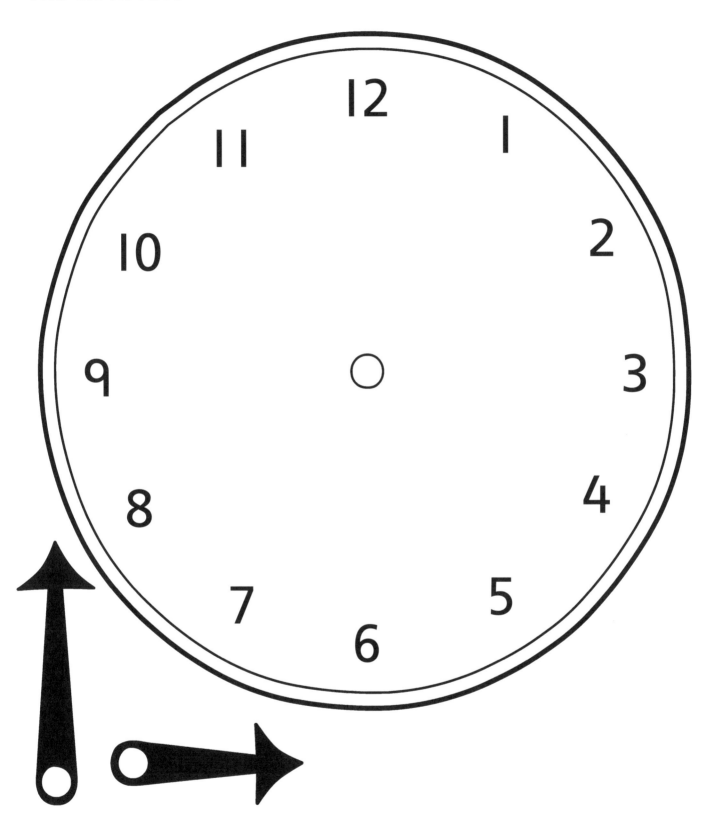

Notes for teachers

Target: Compare and order numbers; read and write numbers from 0 to at least 20 – position these on a number line and a number track (Strand 2). Use vocabulary related to time; read time to hour and half-hour (Strand 6).

Photocopy and laminate this sheet then cut out the clock face and the hour hand or help the child to cut them out. The hands can be positioned by use of sticky-tack. Discuss these with the child – you may like to discuss the day's events starting with 7 or 8 o'clock. The times can be matched to the time cards created from Resource sheets G, H, I and J.

Clock numbers

1	2	3	4
5	6	7	8
9	10	11	12

Days of the week

Monday	Tuesday	Wednesday
Thursday	Friday	Saturday
Sunday		

Notes for teachers

Target: Say and use the number names in order; recognise numerals 1 to 9; numbers from 0 to 12 (Strand 2).
Use vocabulary related to time; read time to hour and half-hour (Strand 6).
These numbers can be cut out to fit in the gaps on the clocks on Worksheets 38 and 39.
The days of the week cards are really useful for children who need to practise getting the days in the right order.